Richard Scarry's
Best Word Book Ever

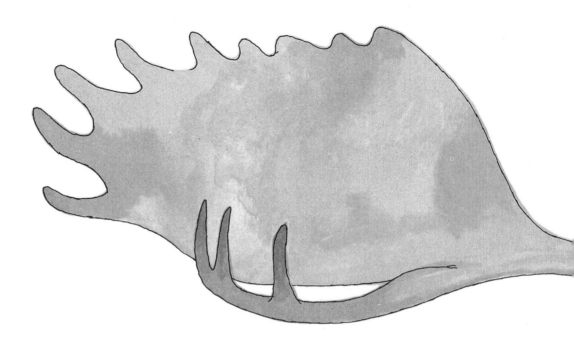

mosquito

First published in hardback in the UK by HarperCollins *Publishers* in 1980
This edition published by HarperCollins *Children's Books* in 2013

HarperCollins *Children's Books* is a division of HarperCollins *Publishers* Ltd,
77-85 Fulham Palace Road, London W6 8JB

1 3 5 7 9 10 8 6 4 2

ISBN: 978-0-00-793528-4

The HarperCollins website address is www.harpercollins.co.uk

Printed and bound in China.

moth

moose

Richard Scarry's
Best
Word Book
Ever

mouse

mushroom

moss

HarperCollins *Children's Books*

The Alphabet

The alligator is eating an apple.
The goose is wearing gloves.
What is the xiphias doing?

A alligator

B bear

C cat

D dog

E egg

F fish

G goose

H heart

I ice cream cone

J

jacket

K kangaroo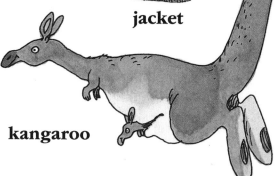

L letter

M mailbag

N nut

O owl

P present

Q queen

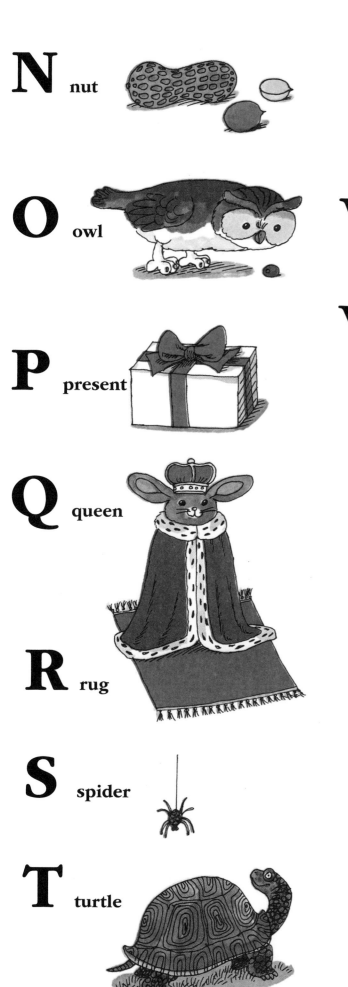

R rug

S spider

T turtle

U umbrella

V vase

W walrus

X xiphias

xylophone

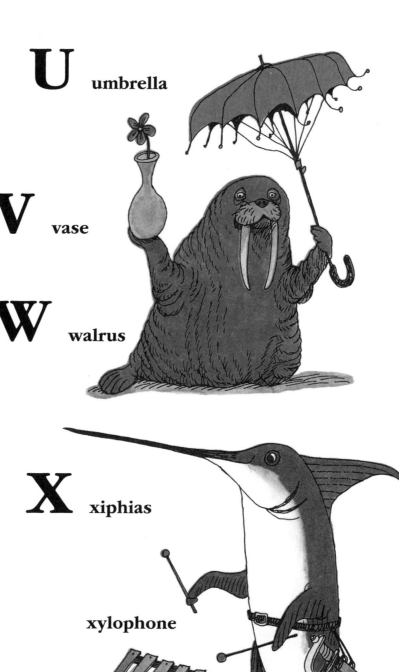

Y yarn

Z zip

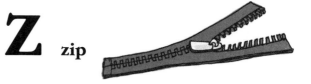

curtains

sun

window

The New Day

It is the morning of a new day.
The sun is shining.
Kenny Bear gets up out of bed.

flannel

soap

towel

First he washes his
face and hands.

toothbrush

toothpaste

Then he brushes
his teeth.

mirror

comb

pyjamas

He combs his hair.

shirt

trousers

He dresses himself.

He makes his bed.

He goes to the kitchen
to eat his breakfast.

Kenny Bear sits in
his favourite chair.

He is very hungry.
This is what he eats —

cold fruit juice

warm cereal

with milk

pancakes

with butter and maple syrup

He doesn't
eat the
toaster.

fried eggs

bacon

toast

muffins

honey

jam

hot chocolate

cool milk

and a waffle.

When he finishes eating breakfast he
helps wash and dry the dishes.

cup   saucer   plate   bowl

fork   knife   spoon   tumbler

lid

jar   jug   frying pan   saucepan   pan   bottle   juice squeezer   glass

Now he is ready to play with his friends.

The Rabbit Family's House

Father Rabbit, Mother Rabbit and the
Rabbit children are getting ready for the
new day. Their friend Owl is waiting
for the children to come outside.
Can you find him?

mirror

lamp

chimney

roof

bed

Big
Brother's
bedroom

cupboard

dining
room

kitchen

table

sink

Father

back door

chair

floor

axe

cooker

Mother

woodpile

lawn

birdbath

smoke

WHOO owl

aerial

light switch

television

record player

foot stool

Mickey

bunk bed

bathroom

Molly

landing

bedroom

front door

living room

candle

outside light

picture

telephone

fireplace

stairs

sofa or couch

hall

doormat

rug

window

stone path

Painting and Drawing with Colours

Painting and drawing are fun. You can use bright colours. You can paint with brushes or even your fingers. You can draw with crayons or pencils. What do you like to draw?

finger painting

paper

make orange

make green

pencil

eraser

pencil drawing

make purple

make pink

make grey

make brown

water dish

watercolours

poster paint

smock

paintbrushes

crayons

pastels

Toys

Sometimes it is fun to play by
yourself. Sometimes it is fun to
play with your friends.
What are your favourite toys?
Do you like to play with blocks?

rocking horse

tricycle

electric train set

truck and loader

blocks

scooter

glider

robot

building set

croquet

At the Playground

The children are all having fun doing different things. Which children are doing the things you like best?

seesaw

slide

leapfrog

somersault

hide-and-seek

ring a ring o'roses

skipping rope

ladder

rings

swing

sliding pole

top

roller skates

bubble blowing

kite

climbing frame

merry-go-round

tag

ring toss

hoop rolling

jacks

marbles

sandpit

kite string

bouncing ball

hopscotch

Tools

hammer

nail

Everyone is very busy working with tools. What tools do you have in your house? What would you like to build?

pushpin

axe

ladder

log

carpenter

board

saw

sawdust

sandpaper

hacksaw

drill

plane

woodpecker

vice

wood shavings

screwdriver

file

screws

pliers

jigsaw

bucksaw

bricklayer

trowel

hoe

brick   brick wall   cement

timber

fence painter

paintbrush

sawhorse

ball of string

paint

ruler

barrel

tack   tack hammer   axe

folding ruler

penknife

toolbox

square

putty knife

shovel

bolt   nut

dirt

monkey wrench

compass

wheelbarrow

pick

glue

haystack

cow

apple tree

farmhouse

water pump

meadow

ence

sheep

horse

apple

grass

clothesline

clothes basket

The Bears' Farm

Kenny Bear is going to feed the chickens.

The Bears are working hard on their farm. What are they all doing? What is the duck doing? What is the scarecrow supposed to be doing? He is not doing it, is he?

chicken coop

well

duck pond

duck   ducklings

bee

pitchfork

beehive

weather instruments

blimp

microphone

control tower

helicopter

At the Airport

The air traffic controller is talking to the pilot of the jet passenger plane. The controller is giving the pilot take-off instructions.

baggage train

waiting room

binoculars

tourist

camera

observation deck

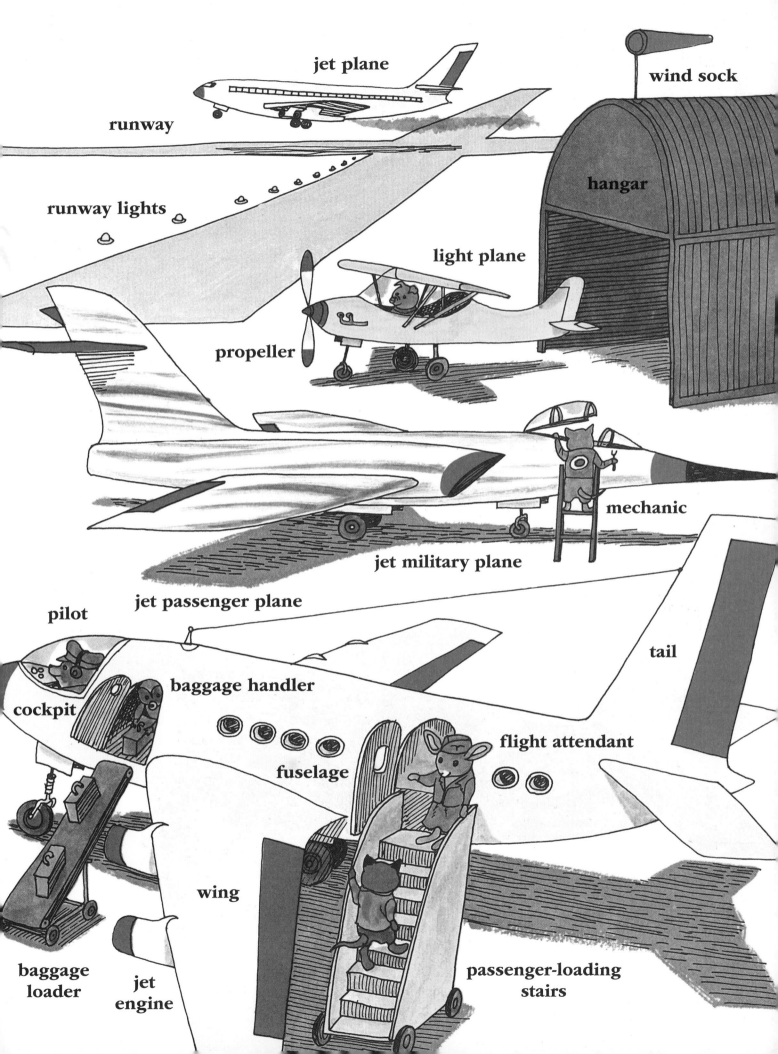

jet plane

wind sock

runway

hangar

runway lights

light plane

propeller

mechanic

jet military plane

jet passenger plane

pilot

tail

baggage handler

cockpit

flight attendant

fuselage

wing

baggage loader

jet engine

passenger-loading stairs

MEATS

hook

saw

scales

brown paper

string

ham

pickle barrel

meat cleaver

butcher

mince

salami

sausages

rubbish bin

fish

bacon

chop

steak

a piglet who wants to work in the supermarket when she grows up

trolley

sawdust

At the Supermarket

The Pigs are buying groceries for their family.
What would you like to buy the next time
you go to the supermarket?
Would you like to buy a pickle?

shopper

books

BOOKS ARE FUN!

customer

orange juice

raisins

money

purse

cashier

eggs

milk

till

ice cream

butter

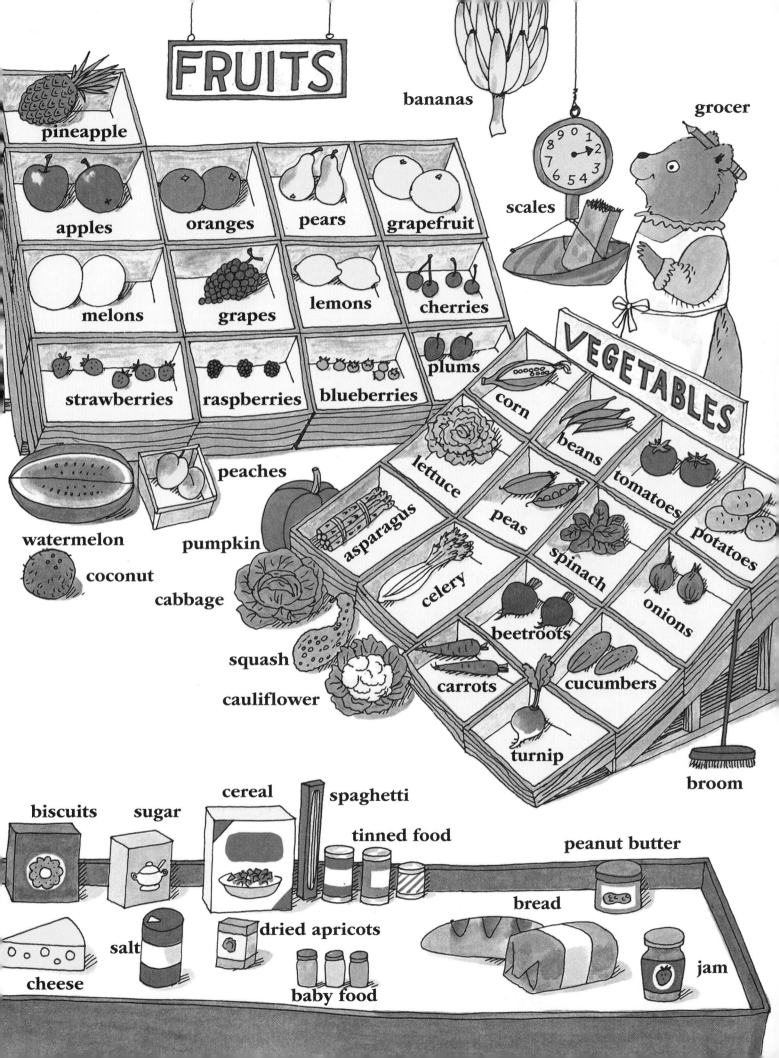

Meal time

The Pig family is having a special celebration meal. There is so much good food to enjoy! What do you see on the table that you like to eat?

carving knife and fork

roast beef

meat platter

tablespoon

coffeepot

salt shaker

teapot

pepper pot

fork

dinner plate

glass

cream jug

cup

knife

spoon

saucer

napkin

sugar bowl

turkey

cake

milk jug

baked potatoes

green beans

jelly

pumpkin mash

cranberry sauce

mashed potatoes

onions

beetroots

ice cream

peas

butter

steak

soup

pie

salad

white bread

brown bread

rolls

submarine

smokestack

stern

bow

ocean liner

police boat

tugboat

barge

pirate ship

ferry

Boats and Ships

One of the things in the water is not a boat, but it helps boats to find the place they want to go. Do you know what it is?

motorboat

paddle

canoe

kayak

oar

rowing boat

freighter

lightship

AMBROSE

coast guard ship

CG-7

oil tanker

fireboat

F.D.

fishing nets

fishing trawler

sport-fishing boat

speedboat

10

houseboat

raft

THE WHITE SWAN

sailing boat

light buoy

2

Keeping Healthy

Your doctor and your dentist are your good friends.
They want you to stay healthy and strong.
Will you give your doctor and dentist a big smile the next
time you see them? How big a smile can you smile?

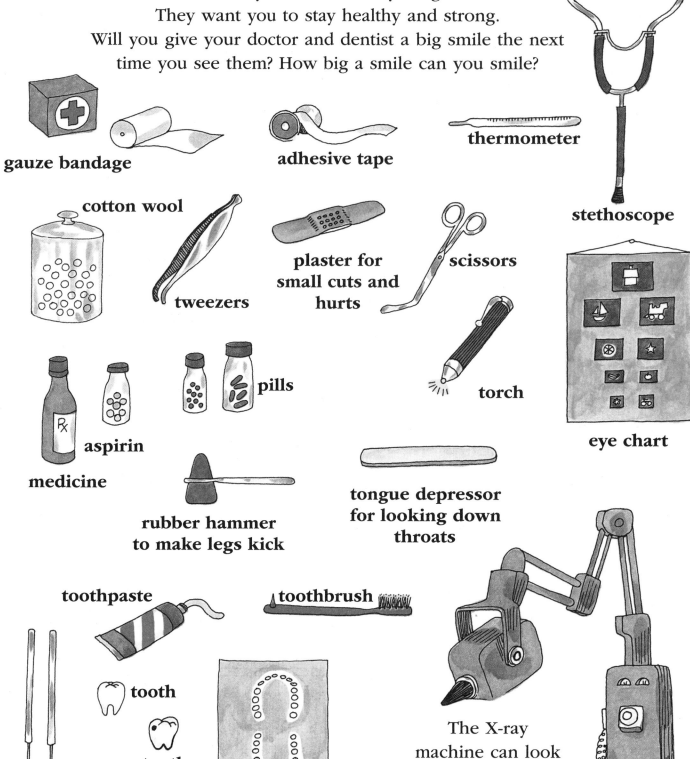

gauze bandage

adhesive tape

thermometer

stethoscope

cotton wool

tweezers

plaster for small cuts and hurts

scissors

pills

torch

eye chart

aspirin

medicine

rubber hammer to make legs kick

tongue depressor for looking down throats

toothpaste

toothbrush

tooth

tooth with a cavity

dental tools

record chart to show where any cavities have been found

The X-ray machine can look inside your tooth to see if anything is wrong with it.

The doctor listens to your heart.

scales

hurt tail

doctor

patient

optician

The optician tests your eyes.

dentist

rinse bowl

instrument table

water cup

dental unit

dentist's chair

dental hygienist

The dentist looks for cavities and the dental hygienist explains how to care for your teeth.

The Bear Twins Get Dressed

Kenny Bear wakes up one cold, frosty morning.
He wants to dress very warmly before going outside.
He yawns and gets up out of bed. He takes off his
pyjamas, folds them, and puts them in a drawer.

What should he wear today to keep warm?

slippers

pyjama top

pyjama bottoms

trousers

dungarees

He puts on his

T-shirt

underpants

cap

shirt

tie

jumper

socks

hat

scarf

trainers

gloves

jacket

overcoat

raincoat

and rainhat.

As Kenny is walking out of the
front door his father says,
"Don't forget to put your boots on!"

boots

 Kathy Bear stretches hard before she gets out of bed. She takes off her nightdress and hangs it on the hook in her wardrobe.

What do you think Kathy should wear today to keep warm?

nightdress

pants

vest

hair ribbon

She puts on her

blouse

skirt

jumper

socks

ear muffs

shoes

snowsuit

and mittens

She puts her purse

into her backpack.

As Kathy is walking out of the front door her mother says, "Don't forget to put your boots on!"

Do you ever forget to put on your boots?

deer

lion

elephant

tiger

monkeys

panda

polar bear

brown bear

gorilla

buffalo

camel

zebra

fish

zookeeper

giraffe

leopard

sea lion

zoo train

At the Zoo

The vet makes sure all the animals are healthy.

Mr. and Mrs. Mouse took their children to the zoo.
How will the children ever be able to get all those balloons into their house tonight?
Which is your favourite animal at the zoo?

rhinoceros

hippopotamus

balloon seller

BOOK PUBLISHER

COSTUMES

skyscraper

aerial

church

NEWSPAPER OFFICE

Dancing School

traffic lights

flats

Bookshop

telephone box

CHEMIST

postbox

book reader

street

postman

post van

In the City

Mouse has just bought a book from the bookshop. She is going to buy a newspaper and then join her rabbit friends at the café and drink some lemonade with them. Show with your finger the way she will go. Remember to have her look both ways before she crosses a road.

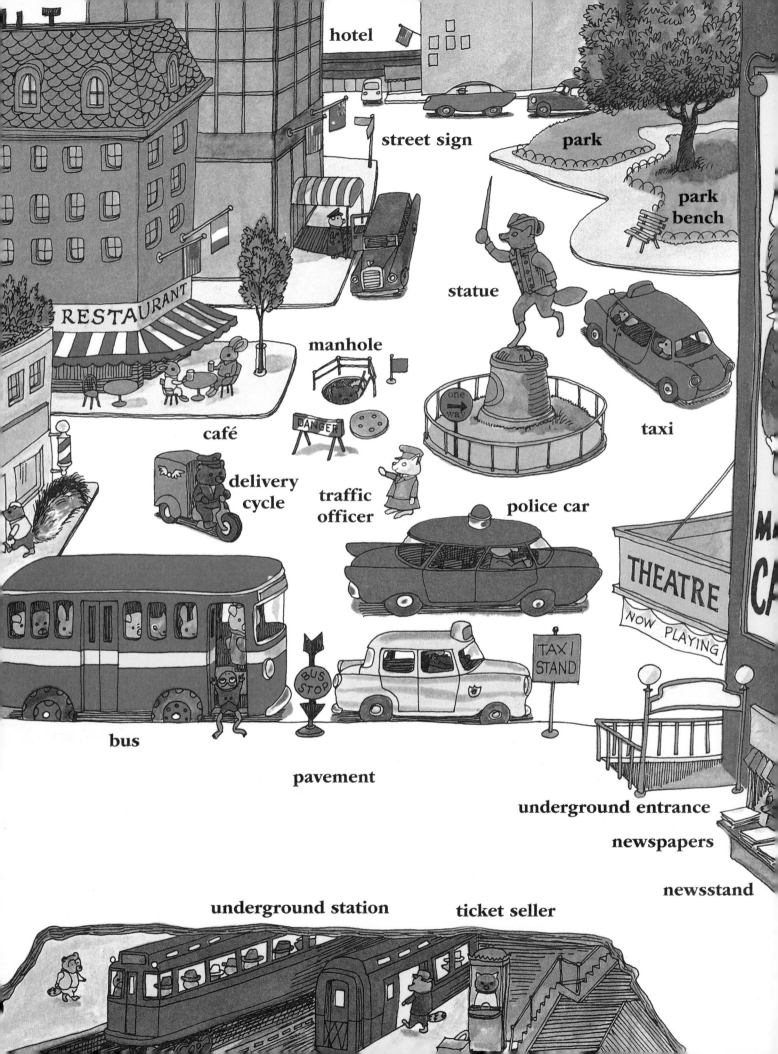

hotel

street sign

park

park bench

statue

taxi

RESTAURANT

manhole

DANGER

one way

café

delivery cycle

traffic officer

police car

THEATRE

NOW PLAYING

bus

BUS STOP

TAXI STAND

pavement

underground entrance

newspapers

newsstand

underground station

ticket seller

A Drive in the Country

There are many things to see when you take a drive in the country. Can you see Harry and Sally, the mountain climbers? Can you see what Harry has dropped from his backpack?

radio tower

island

ocean

factory

lake

petrol station

tunnel

petrol pump

tollbooth

motorway

bridge

farm

brook

mill

stream

waterfall

picnic area

picnickers

lighthouse

beach

bay

woods

seaport

hill

windmill

pond

road

crane

fire lookout tower

drawbridge

tug

mountain

village

river

log cabin

mountain climbers

cliff

forest

backpack

apple

Holidays

Holidays are happy times, aren't they?
Which holiday do you like best?
I bet you like them all.
On holidays we visit friends and relatives.
Sometimes we give or get presents.
What would you like to get for your birthday?

New Year's Day

St. Valentine's Day

Easter

horn

valentine

Easter egg

Easter bunny

Easter chick

Birthday

balloons

rattle

cake

ice cream

Halloween

ghost

skeleton

witch

moon

black cat

witch's broom

pumpkin

trick-or-treat bag

Hanukkah

menorah

angel

candle

wreath

Christmas

Christmas tree

stockings

holly

decorations

tree lights

beard

fireplace

sack

Father Christmas

present

At School

School is fun. There are so many things we learn to do. Kathy Bear is learning how to find a lost mitten.

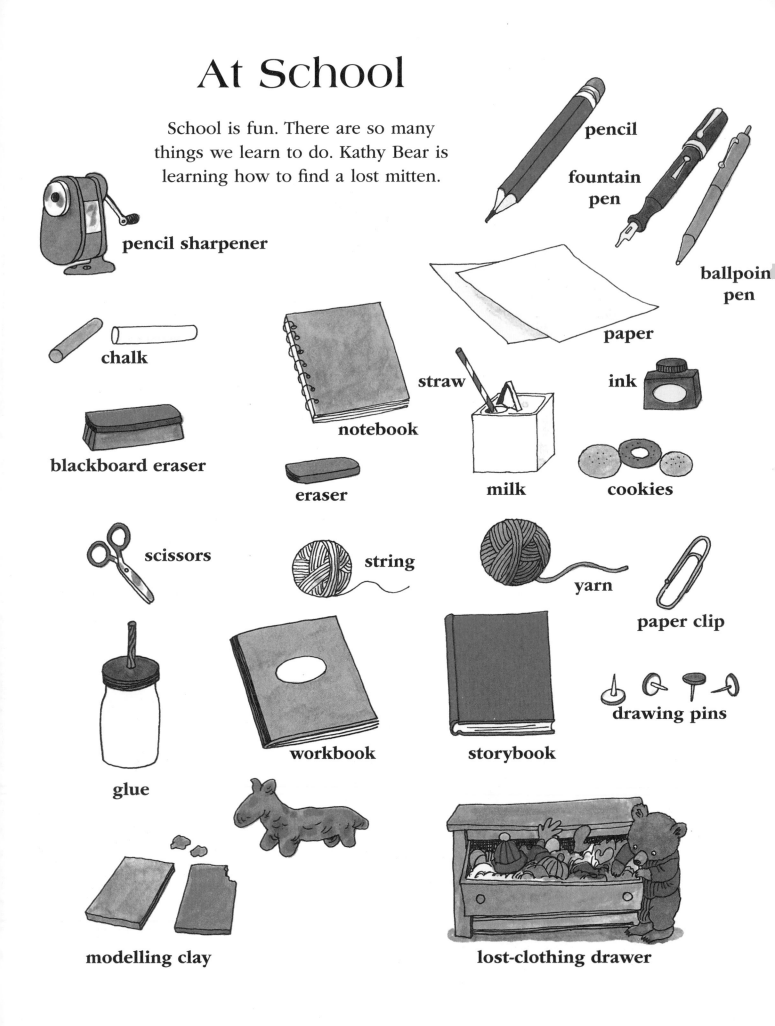

pencil

fountain pen

ballpoin pen

pencil sharpener

paper

chalk

straw

ink

blackboard eraser

notebook

eraser

milk

cookies

scissors

string

yarn

paper clip

glue

workbook

storybook

drawing pins

modelling clay

lost-clothing drawer

flag

clock

bell

blackboard

calendar

teacher

JANUARY

a b c

cat dog

map

map stand

inkwell

wastepaper
basket

artist

pupil

desk

classroom

paper shapes

music
teacher

refrigerator

kitchen cabinet

doorknob

can opener

soap

teapot

socket

counter

dishwasher

freezer

bin

washing machine

egg whisk

Father Pig

laundry basket

eggshell

stool

Annie Pig

mixing bowl

spoon

measuring jug

rolling pin

Susan Pig

cookie cutter

dough

Peter Pig

sieve

cake pan

funnel

cookie tray

spatula

ketchup bottle

flour bin

sugar bowl

mustard jar

food grinder

cupboard

feather duster

dustpan

mop

broom

vacuum cleaner

egg timer

shelf

cooker hood

Mother Pig

coffeepot

kettle

oven

iron

ironing board

In the Kitchen

All the Pigs like to work in the kitchen.
They are making good things to eat.
What is Father Pig making?
What is Mother Pig putting into the oven?

teaspoon

tablespoon

soup spoon

double boiler

blender

pestle

toaster

mortar

saucepan

corkscrew

ladle

colander

matches

measuring spoons

cutting board

potato masher

pepper grinder

salt shaker

electric mixer

cookery book

carving fork and knife

When You Grow Up

What would you like to be when you are bigger?
Would you like to be a chef?
Would you like to be a doctor or a nurse?
What would you like to be?

police officer

firefighter

sailor

nurse

taxi driver

farmer

gardener

doctor   **carpenter**

musician

scientist

baker

dentist

secretary

chef

singer

artist

pilot

angler

truck driver

teacher

garage mechanic

judge

reporter

photographer

shopkeeper

librarian

dancer

daddy

mummy

Things We Do

There are many things that we can do.
And there are some things we cannot do.
What is the one thing we can't do?
Look and see.

dig

blow

build

break

sleep

wake up

walk

run

stand

sit

read

watch

draw and write

pull

push

kick

talk

listen

shout

whisper

eat

laugh

smile

cry

drink

jump over

crawl under

fall down

we can't fly

peek

tip a hat

go up

go down

go in

come out

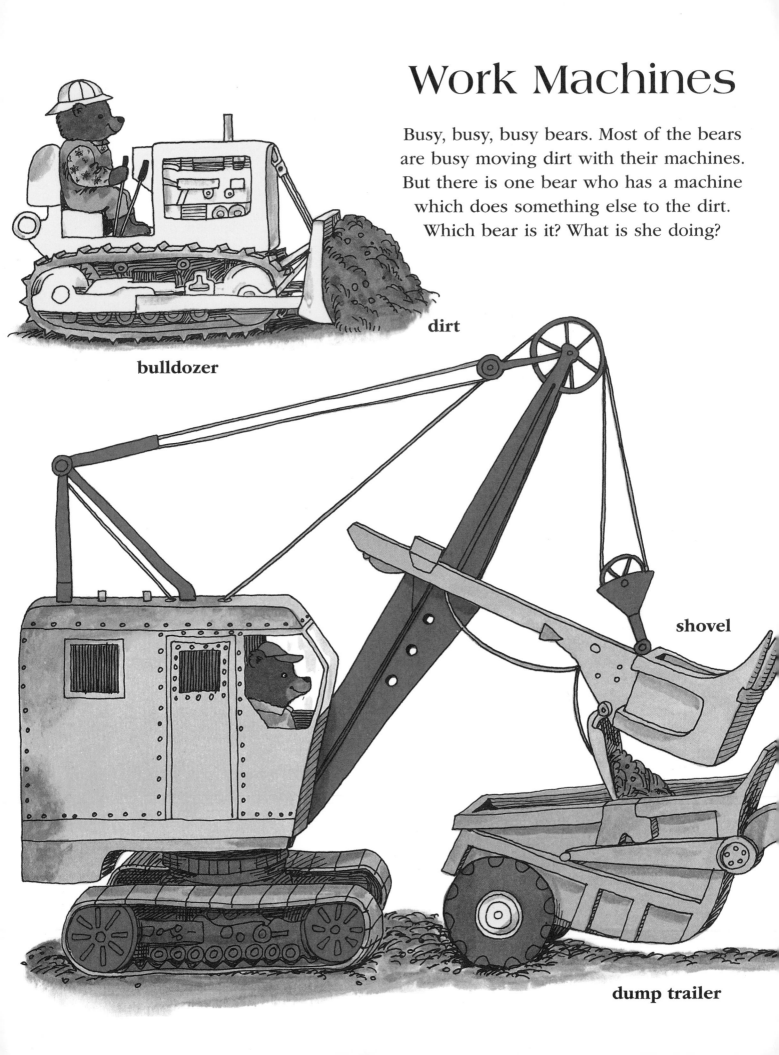

Work Machines

Busy, busy, busy bears. Most of the bears are busy moving dirt with their machines. But there is one bear who has a machine which does something else to the dirt. Which bear is it? What is she doing?

dirt

bulldozer

shovel

dump trailer

tractor scraper

tractor shovel

dump truck

bucket loader

dirt

roller

and tractor

smooth dirt

rough dirt

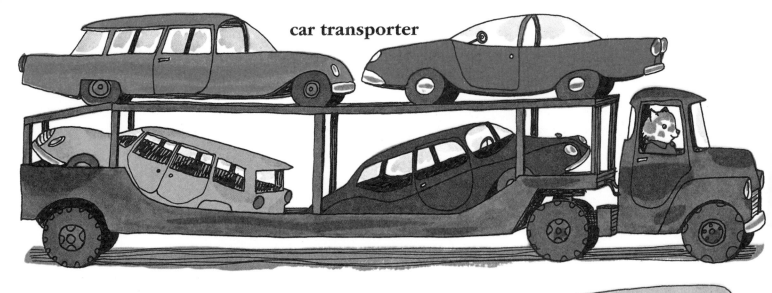

car transporter

milk van

petrol truck

broken-down car

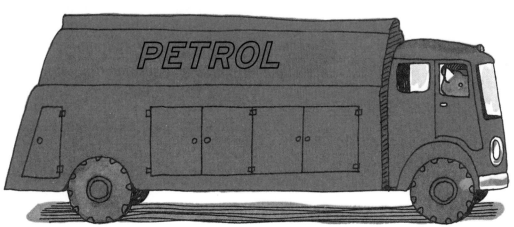

motorcycle

tow truck

taxi

sports car

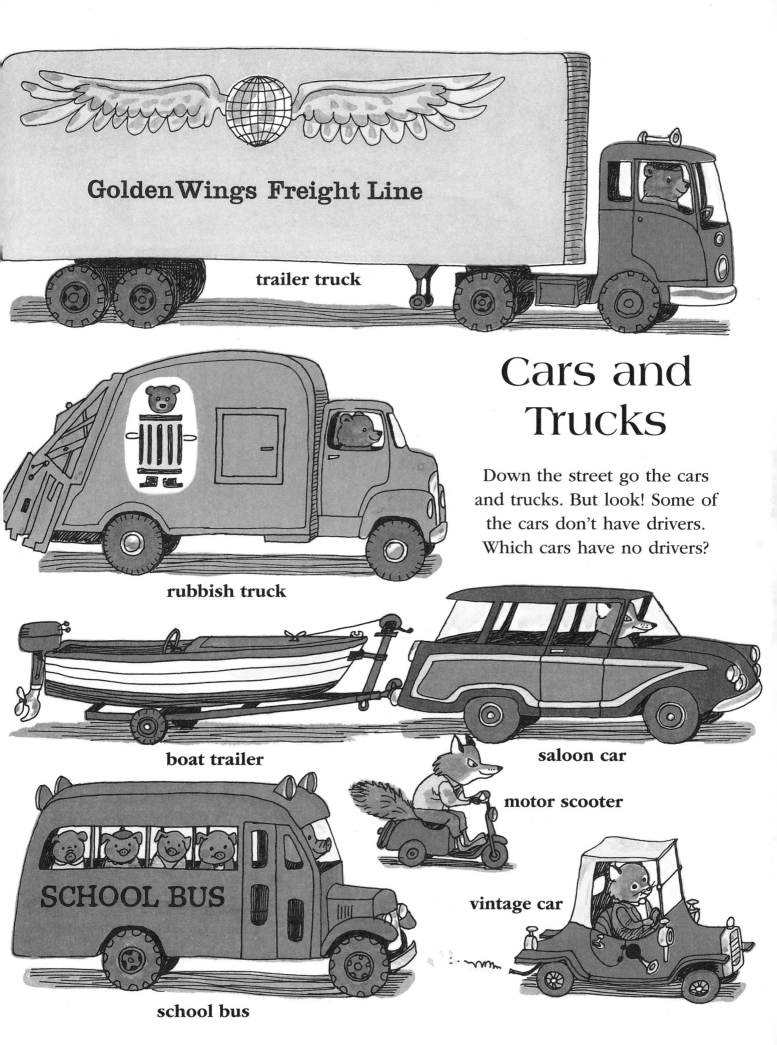

GoldenWings Freight Line

trailer truck

rubbish truck

boat trailer

school bus

Cars and Trucks

Down the street go the cars and trucks. But look! Some of the cars don't have drivers. Which cars have no drivers?

saloon car

motor scooter

vintage car

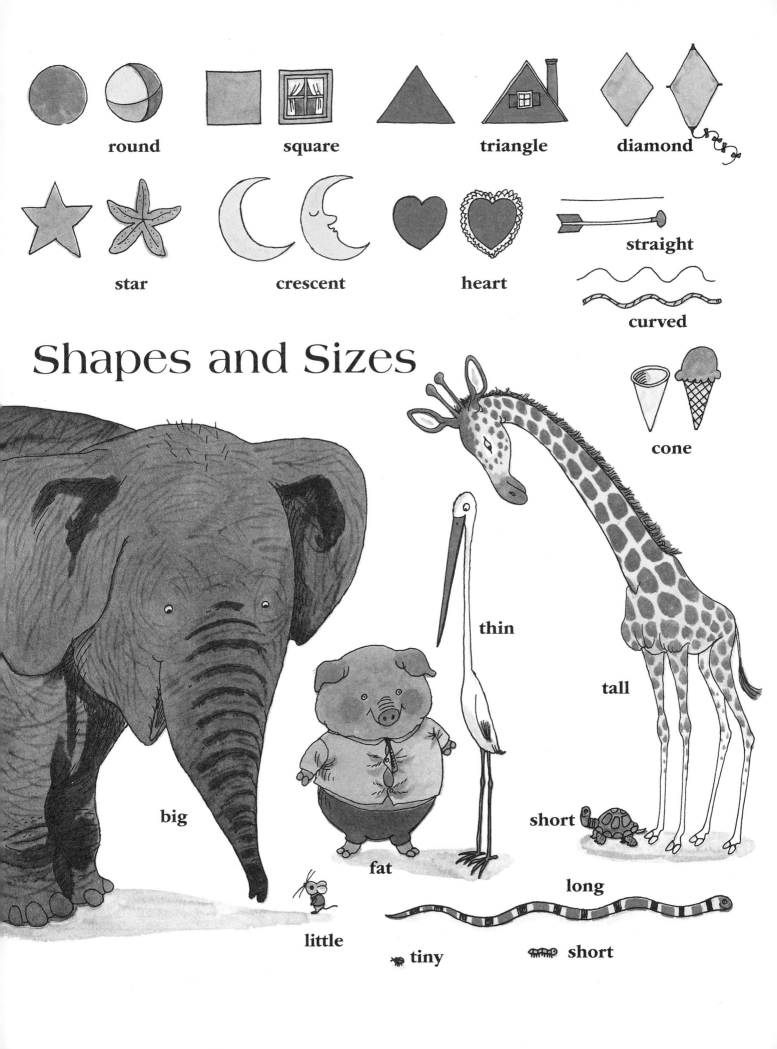

round

square

triangle

diamond

star

crescent

heart

straight

curved

Shapes and Sizes

cone

thin

tall

big

fat

short

long

little

tiny

short

father   mother

The Baby

The Cat family has a new baby kitten.
They don't know what to name it.
What would you like to
name the new baby?
Write the kitten's name here.

—— —— —— —— ——   uncle

grandmother

baby   bottle

rattle   brother

nappy

sister   aunt

grandfather   playpen   cousin

high chair   pushchair

cot

Moses
basket

play table   walker   buggy

At the Circus

The band is playing and the animals are doing their acts.
What do you like to watch best at the circus?

tent pole

balancing pole

tightrope performer

tightrope

band

horse rider

rope ladder

bandstand

circus horse

elephant

sawdust

ring

trick dog

clown

ringmaster

flag

circus tent

trapeze

trapeze artist

safety net

acrobat

ticket seller

hoop

lion

cage

lion tamer

juggler

sea lion

popcorn seller

balloon seller

The Firefighters to the Rescue

Will the brave firefighters put out the fire in time? I think so, don't you?

rescue truck

police car

nozzle

fire engine

rear-wheel steerer

hook-and-ladder truck

hose

ladder

front-wheel steerer

fire alarm box

boots

hook

bell

helmet

first-aid kit

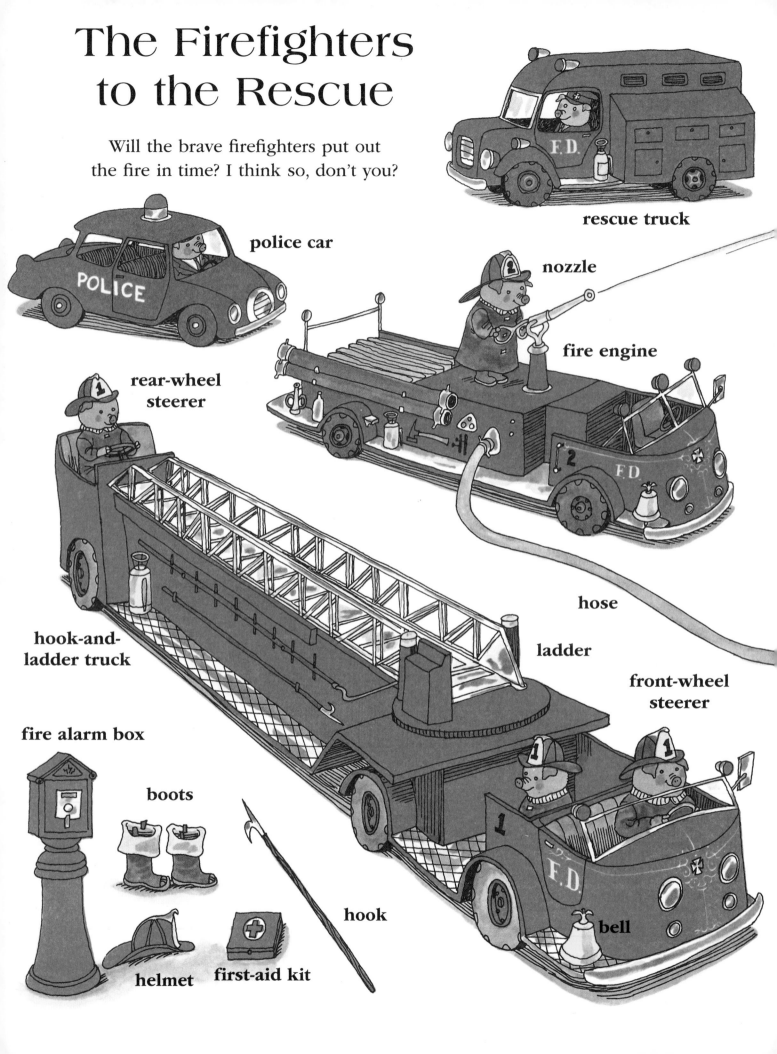

ambulance

flames

water

smoke

fire chief

megaphone

cat in danger

fire chief's car

firefighter

pumper

fire hydrant

ladder

firefighters

rescue net

firefighter

fire extinguisher

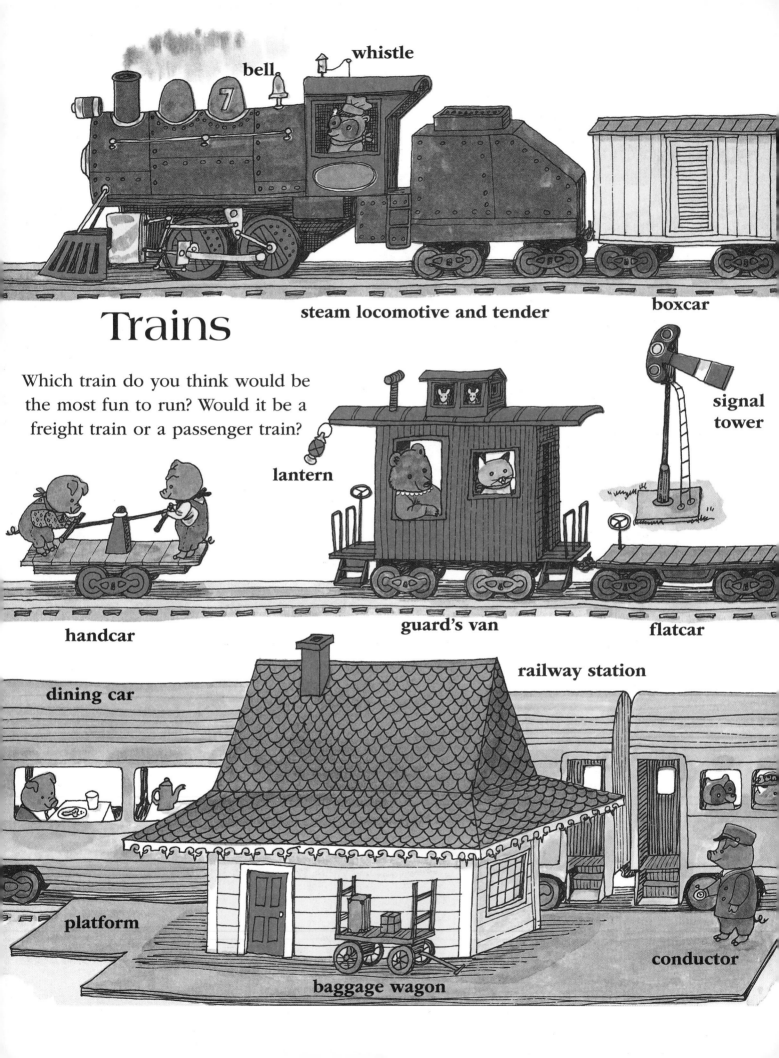

bell

whistle

steam locomotive and tender

boxcar

Trains

Which train do you think would be the most fun to run? Would it be a freight train or a passenger train?

lantern

signal tower

handcar

guard's van

flatcar

dining car

railway station

platform

baggage wagon

conductor

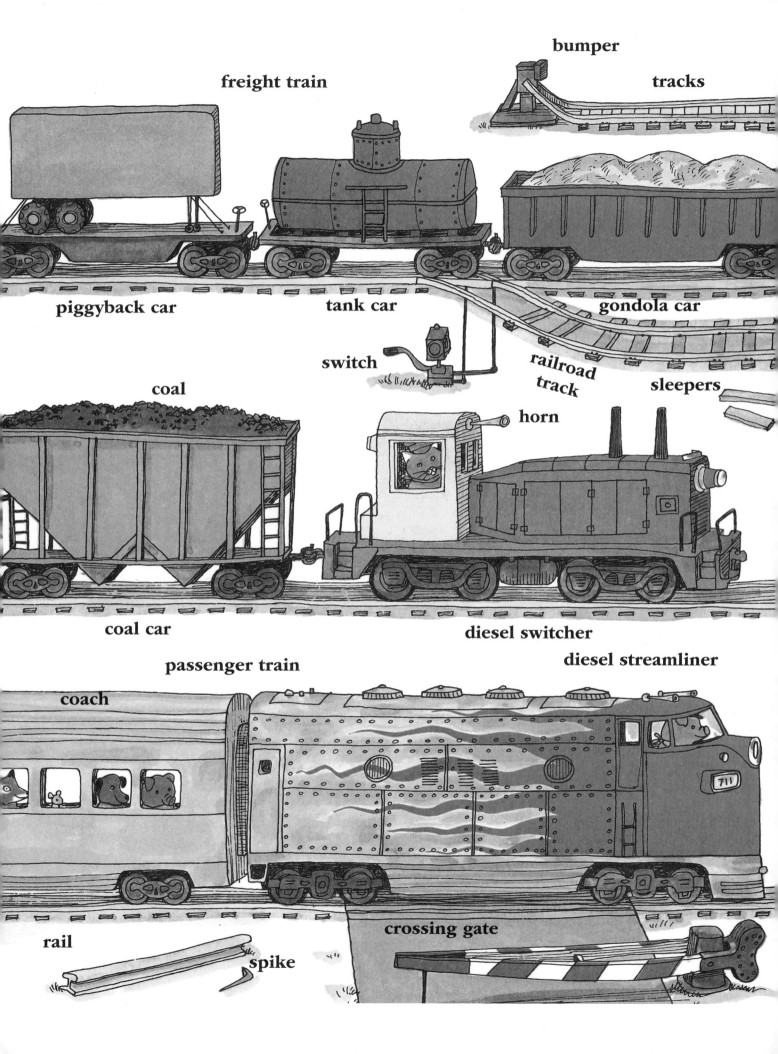

bumper

tracks

freight train

piggyback car

tank car

gondola car

switch

railroad
track

sleepers

coal

horn

coal car

diesel switcher

diesel streamliner

passenger train

coach

crossing gate

rail

spike

At the Beach

In the summertime it is fun to go to the beach. What do you think Rabbit hears in the seashell? Is it the sound of the waves?

telescope

lighthouse

oar

anchor

beach toy

spade

rowing boat

sandpiper

sand castle

skate

bluefish

oyster

lobster

scallop

hermit crab

clam

Making Things Grow

Everyone is working in the garden.
Mr. Crow has a seed in his mouth.
Do you think he will plant it?
Or will he eat it?

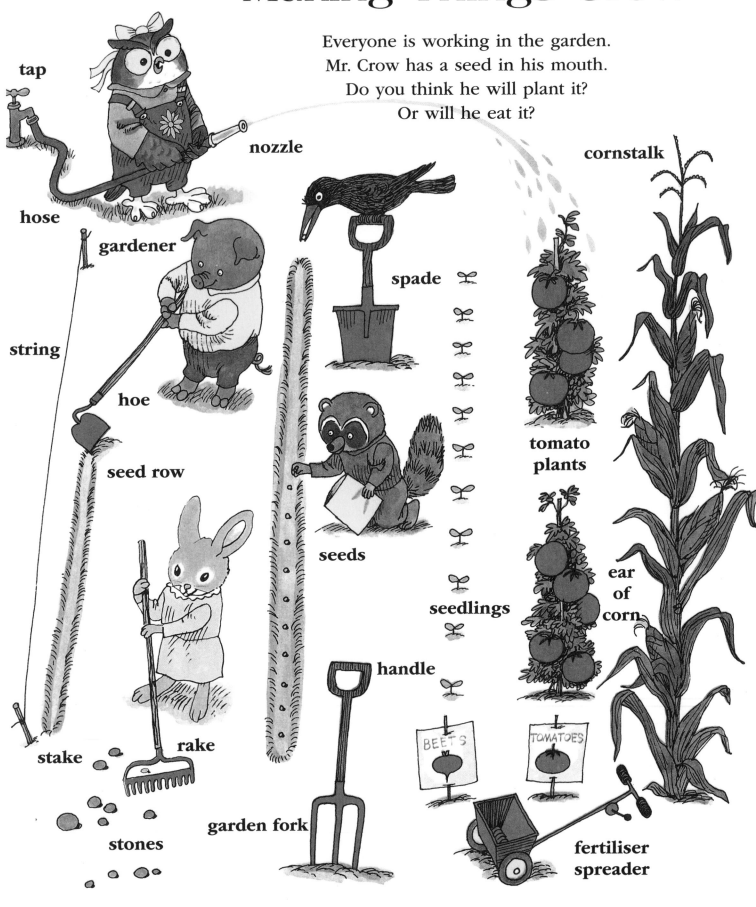

tap

nozzle

cornstalk

hose

gardener

spade

tomato
plants

string

hoe

seed row

seeds

ear
of
corn

rake

seedlings

handle

stake

garden fork

BEETS

TOMATOES

stones

fertiliser
spreader

The Weather

When we go outdoors we see what the weather is like. Sometimes it is sunny. Sometimes it is cloudy. It can be windy, or cold, or hot. It can be snowing or raining. What was the weather like outdoors today? What is your favourite kind of weather?

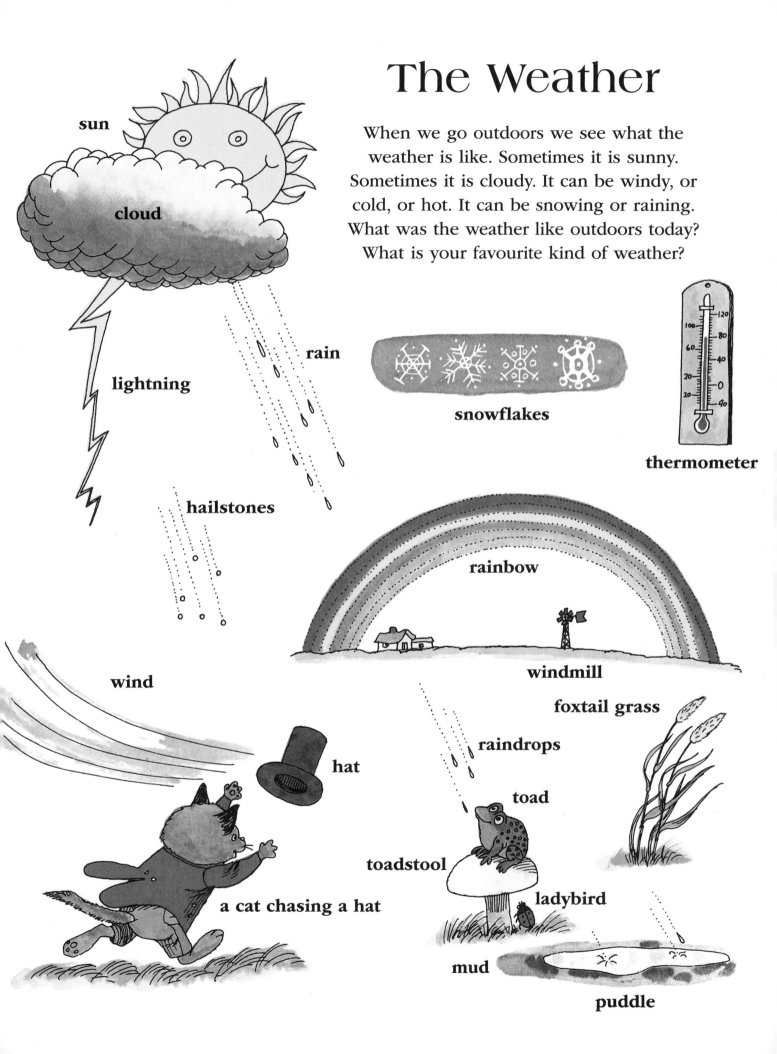

sun

cloud

lightning

rain

hailstones

snowflakes

thermometer

rainbow

windmill

wind

hat

foxtail grass

raindrops

toad

toadstool

ladybird

a cat chasing a hat

mud

puddle

kite

rain shower

plough

buds   robin

nest

Spring

Look at that baby lamb hop!
It is spring. She is happy.
Look at Mr. Bear coming out of his cave!
It is spring. He is happy.
Now he can use his new lawn mower.

tree

lamb

bush

bridge

brook

cave

fern

roots

turtle

frog

pussy willow

daffodils

lawn mower

violets

crocus

cow

meadow

calf

cornfield

fence

Summer

Do you like to go on picnics
in the summertime?
Ants just love to go to picnics.
Do you know why?

tent

car

fly

screen

barbeque

charcoal

picnic basket   cooler

hamburger

charcoal bag

ketchup

hotdog

mosquito

pole

paper cup

pickle

mustard

rock

ants

float

cattails

frog

deck

pond

water lily

dragonfly

pebbles

stones

sun

duck

falling leaves

corn stock

stone wall

pumpkin

nuts

gate

roadside stand

apple juice

corn

jam

Autumn

In the autumn the air gets colder. The green leaves turn to bright colours. Then they fall to the ground.

squash

basket of apples

smoke

turkey

flames

rake

bonfire

leaves

Winter

There are many ways to have fun on the snow and ice. Maybe you would like to do all of them. Would you?

snowstorm

sleigh

icicle

fishing shack

skis

sledge

toboggan

ice fishing

snow

ice-skating rink

ice skater

snowball

hockey stick

puck

ice skates

scarf

spare tyre

jeep

snowplough

a pig all wrapped up

snowman

Little Things

Here are many little things.
What little things do you sometimes
put on your bedroom wall?

 worm

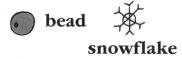 button

 dandelion seed

spool

thread

 fly

 ant

 drop of water

 ladybird

bead

 snowflake

pin

 fingerprint

 petal

 mosquito

 butterfly

fish-hook

crumb

 bubble

 peanut

 tack

 pen nib

tea leaf

gumdrop

pea

 caterpillar

 jelly bean

 firefly

ring

sand

blueberry

 moth

 rice

 tadpole

keyhole

 shell

marble

blade of grass

 paper clip

 cricket

 raisin

 beetle

 raspberry

thimble

pincushion

 hermit crab

pebble

 sea horse

 bee

mushroom

pearl

 ink spot

 confetti

 feather

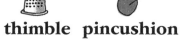 splinter

 bean

 safety pin

 baby mouse

dot

Parts of the Body

Bears use their paws to pick things up.
What do you use?

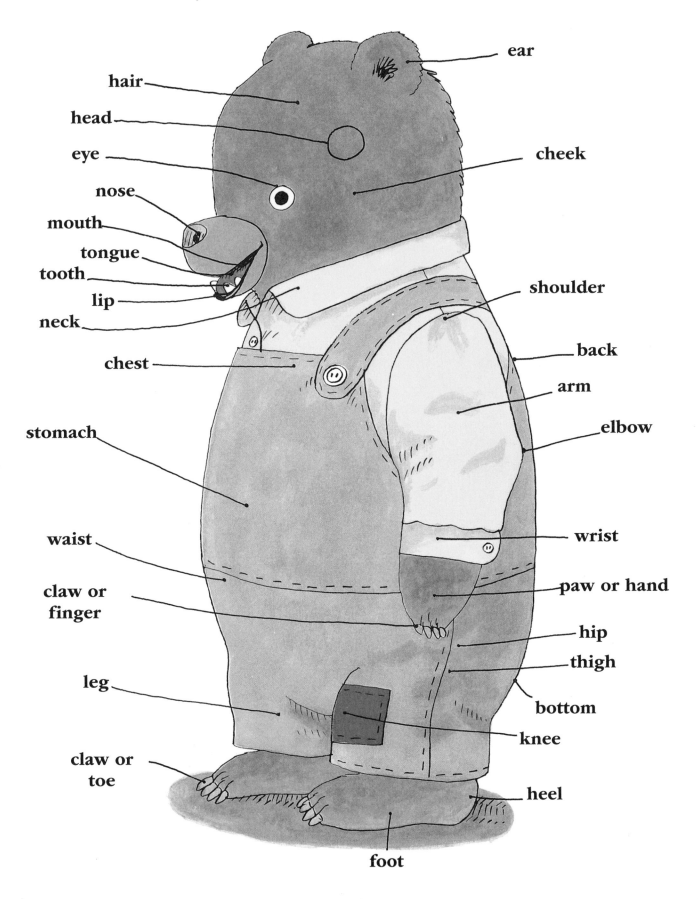

hair

head

eye

nose

mouth

tongue

tooth

lip

neck

chest

stomach

waist

claw or
finger

leg

claw or
toe

ear

cheek

shoulder

back

arm

elbow

wrist

paw or hand

hip

thigh

bottom

knee

heel

foot

Bedtime

Little Elephant is getting ready for bed.
But who is that hiding under the bed?
Find that rascal and tell her to brush
her teeth and get ready for bed, too.

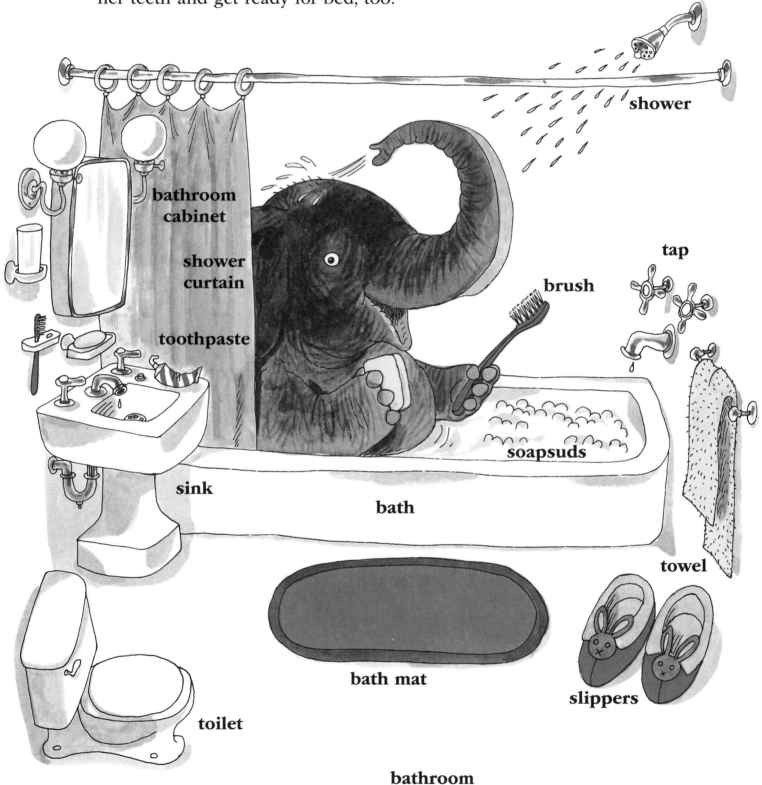

shower

bathroom cabinet

shower curtain

tap

brush

toothpaste

soapsuds

sink

bath

towel

bath mat

slippers

toilet

bathroom

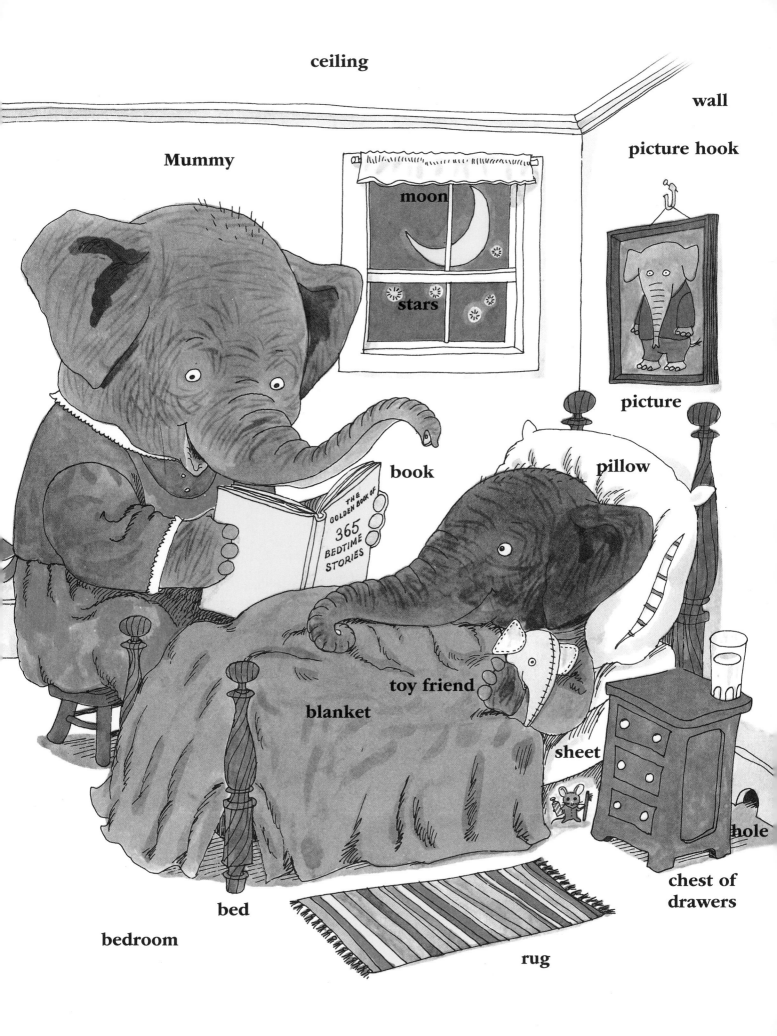

ceiling

wall

picture hook

Mummy

moon

stars

picture

book

pillow

THE GOLDEN BOOK OF
365
BEDTIME
STORIES

toy friend

blanket

sheet

hole

bed

chest of drawers

bedroom

rug

Numbers

How high can you count?
Can you count up to twenty ladybirds?
I'll bet you can.

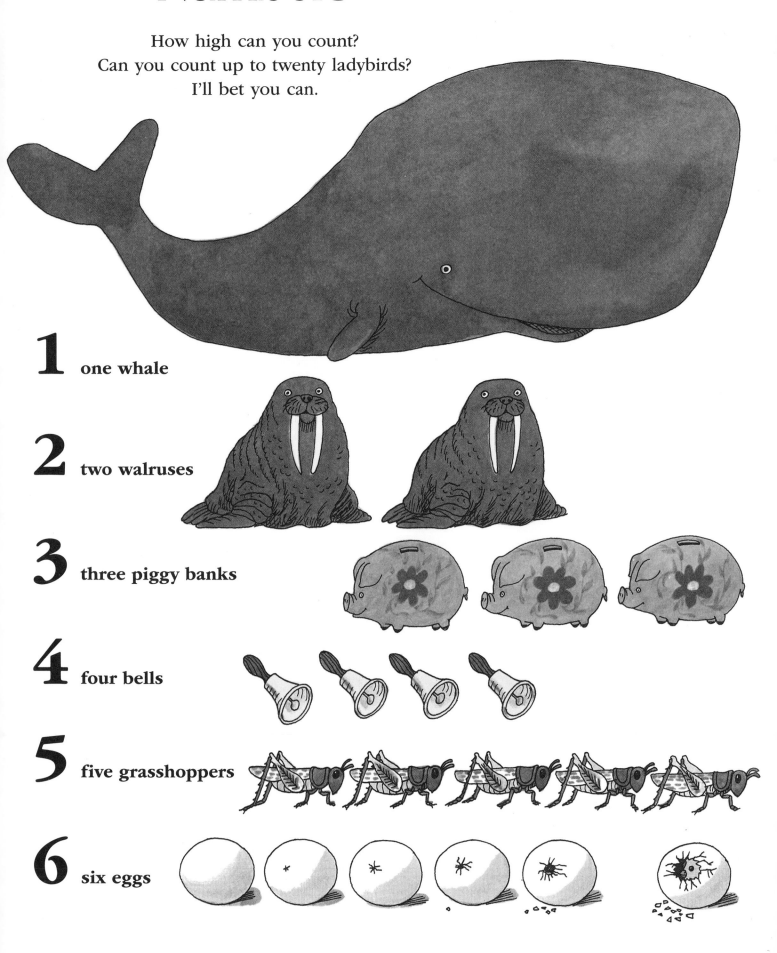

1 one whale

2 two walruses

3 three piggy banks

4 four bells

5 five grasshoppers

6 six eggs

7 seven caterpillars

8 eight spools

9 nine spiders

10 ten keys

11 eleven ants

12 twelve rings

13 thirteen gumdrops

14 fourteen leaves

15 fifteen snowflakes

16 sixteen acorns

17 seventeen pins

18 eighteen buttons

19 nineteen beads

20 twenty ladybirds

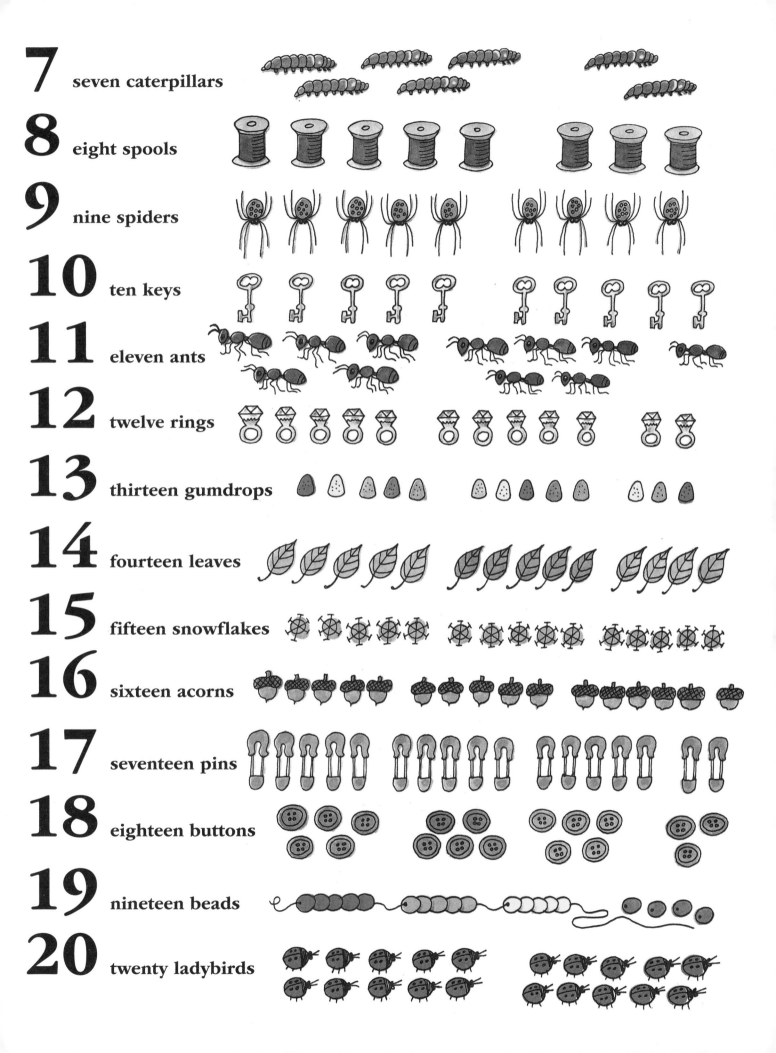